Talking together...

about growing up

a workbook for parents of children with learning disabilities

**Lorna Scott
& Lesley Kerr-Edwards**

fpa

putting sexual health on
the agenda

Acknowledgements

The authors would like to thank all the people have made this book possible.

Joanna Laxton of **fpa** Cymru who identified a very real need for this book through her groundbreaking work on the Sex Education in Special Schools Project in 1992/3.

The parents, staff and headteachers of the schools which took part in the initial discussion and trials of these materials. They were enthusiastic and supportive of the project throughout:
Elmwood School, Bridgwater
Milton School, Glasgow
Penrose School, Bridgwater
Verney Avenue School, High Wycombe
Vinio House School, High Wycombe
Ysgol Erw'r Delyn, Penarth

Kim Wyatt, parent

Dr Jackie Rodgers, Imogen Ashby, Sarah Andrews, Joanna Laxton, Simon Blake and Georgie McCormick who commented on the text.

The Image in Action team, upon whose work this book is based. Two activities, 'No, That's Private' and 'Body Fluids', are adapted from *Let's Do It: creative activities for sex education for young people with learning disabilities*, B Johns and others, Image in Action 1997.

fpa gratefully acknowledges funding from the Headley Trust and the Abbey National Charitable Trust towards the production of this book

Talking together... about growing up

is published by **fpa**
2-12 Pentonville Road
London N1 9FP

© **fpa** 1999

British Library Cataloguing in Publication Data
A catalogue record for this book is available from the British Library

ISBN 1 899194 96 7

Illustrations by Nic Watts © Nic Watts
Designed and typeset by Andy Dark
Printed by The Jason Press

Contents

About this book

This book is for you - the parents and families of young people with learning disabilities - so that you can help your children learn about the changes that happen when they are growing up. You are the most important people to do this. You know your child best, and you can give constant help and reminders at home to support what the school is teaching.

Many books have been written about growing up for young people who can read for themselves. This one is different. It's for young people who may not be able to read so well, but who can understand what it's about. They may be in schools for children with severe or moderate learning disabilities, but even within this range there can be big differences. Most of the activities will work with most of the children within this range but not all the activities may suit every child.

The book is for parents with children at the stage of puberty when their bodies start to change, or just before. These changes can happen over a wide age range, although mostly between 11 and 15, so we need to be guided by our own child's development. The last chapter touches on sexual relationships, but this is something for a later stage when children are a bit older. This book is a beginning, not the end!

So, what's in it?

There are seven chapters. The first five are about all the things children need to understand before they can learn about the puberty stage. Things like where they fit into the life cycle (*Chapter 1*) and knowing names of body parts (*Chapter 2*). It's essential for children to understand about public and private (*Chapter 3*). This is closely linked with keeping safe, the subject of *Chapter 4*. **Feelings** (*Chapter 5*) helps children recognise and trust their feelings, which helps them with social skills and relationships, and to avoid uncomfortable or dangerous situations. *Chapter 6* contains all the more intimate aspects of growing up: body changes, periods and masturbation. Finally, we think about the future in terms of sex and relationships in **Looking Ahead** (*Chapter 7*). **Further Information** (page 76) at the end has a glossary of words, addresses of some useful organisations which can give advice and support, and a short list of books which provide more information about children growing up.

Each chapter has an introduction and one or more activities. We've called them activities because they often describe things you can do together, and to stress that children learn best by doing things. Some of these activities could be called games because they are fun to do. It doesn't mean they aren't serious - we learn a lot from repetition, and playing games gives plenty of practice of important skills. Some chapters have picture stories. Stories are a good way of describing some of the more private aspects of growing up; they are talking about someone else so we don't have to be embarrassed by talking about ourselves. They give lots of scope for further discussion - and children enjoy them!

Using the activities at home

The activities don't take long - 10 or 15 minutes at most. Repeat them as often as you need. Repeat the key words and phrases often too. Think about the best time and place – some of the activities may need privacy without other people around. You may find a suitable moment when an opportunity arises: at bathtime, watching a TV soap, or doing the laundry. Think about where the private places in your home are so that you can explain them to your child. Maybe make **'Private'** labels for these places. Encourage your child to make choices at home about everyday things, to increase independence. You can use **The Choice Chart** in *Chapter 4*.

A final word. Let's remember it's perfectly OK for us to say no to our children. They will also learn that it's OK to say no.

Working with your child's school

Every school has a policy about sex education, saying what they teach and when. Ask to see it, and talk to the teacher about it. Let the teacher know if you think your child is ready to learn something that hasn't come up in the school's programme yet. Find out when things are to be taught, so that you can work on the same topics at home. It helps children most if home and school are working together and supporting one another. Also find out what the arrangements are in school for things like changing pads, so that you can prepare and reassure your child.

Ask the school for help if you need it. It's not always easy to help our own children at this time. Many parents find it's useful to get together with other parents to share ideas, worries - and laughs. Schools sometimes arrange this. The school may also have books or videos you can borrow to use at home.

Using a book like this raises a number of questions

Family backgrounds are not all the same, and we haven't been able to represent them all in one book. You will need to tailor it to fit your own circumstances: your beliefs, your family customs, your views on sexual matters. There are some suggestions about ways of doing this in each chapter.

The activities and stories tend to describe 'typical' people, describing what 'most' women or men do for instance. This makes it easier for a less able child to understand the difference between the sexes, but it means that we haven't covered all the differences that our children meet in real life.

Talking about growing up means that we have to think about the words we are going to use about private body parts and sex. Most schools decide to use the 'proper' or biological names. Most parents want their children to learn these names too, but most of us use family names at home. You will have to decide for yourself which words you are going to use. Sorting this out is important so there's a guide on page 76, **Which Words do we Use?**.

As children grow up they are faced with all sorts of new experiences. We can help them to be more independent by trying not to protect them too much. They will learn from these experiences, especially if they are allowed to take some carefully planned risks. We have to work out what we can safely let them do without them getting into real difficulties.

This, of course, brings us to one of our chief anxieties about our learning disabled children, that they can be vulnerable to all sorts of exploitation and abuse. Using these materials with our children can help them to keep themselves safe, so that they know that some parts of their bodies are private, and they learn what to do and say in certain situations. We have to remember that ignorance never protects anyone. But it's our responsibility to make sure that any adults who use these activities with our children respect the child's privacy and rights, and do not take the opportunity to satisfy their own needs.

And finally...

Our hope in writing this book is that parents will find it easier to help their children grow up with confidence. Enjoy using the activities with your children.

Pathways through the book

The chapters have been arranged in a logical order, so you could just work your way through. But you will need to think about your child and his or her present knowledge and needs. You might decide to do a particular activity to support what your child is learning at school at a particular time. Whichever way, you'll find it helps to go back and repeat things, to make sure your child understands and remembers. But you don't have to do everything. Use the book to work for you and your child.

Here are two suggestions to help you to decide where to start with your child.

Pathways for children at different stages suggests using some activities in a particular order to suit different children.

What does your child need to learn? is a quick guide showing which activities can be used to fit different topics. But it's for you to decide how to use the book.

Pathways for children at different stages

<u>For a boy aged 9</u> with severe learning disabilities (before puberty)

- **Family Photos**, Chapter 1

- **Body Shapes**, using the male body outline, in Chapter 2

- **Places**, Chapter 3

- **No, that's Private**, Chapter 3

<u>A girl aged 12</u> with severe learning disabilities who has just started her periods

- **Family Photos**, Chapter 1

- **Body Shapes**, Chapter 2

- **What are Body Fluids?**, Chapter 2

- **Understanding Feelings**, Chapter 5

- **Jenny's Story** - from the **Body Changes Stories** in Chapter 6

- **Cara's Story**, about periods, in Chapter 6

A boy aged 12 with moderate learning disabilities, whose body is starting to develop

- **Family Photos**, Chapter 1
- **Mark's Story** - from **Life Stories** in Chapter 1
- **Body Shapes**, Chapter 2
- **What are Body Fluids**?, Chapter 2
- **No, That's Private**, Chapter 3
- **What Happens Next?**, Chapter 4
- **Understanding Feelings**, Chapter 5
- **Benni's Story** - from the **Body Changes Stories** in Chapter 6
- **Matt's Story** - from the **Private Touching Stories** in Chapter 6

A girl aged 14 with moderate learning disabilities who knows about body changes and hygiene, and wants to become more independent

- **Family Photos**, Chapter 1
- **Mo's Story**, about the responsibilities of growing up, Chapter 1
- **No, That's Private**, Chapter 3
- **What Happens Next?**, Chapter 4
- **Understanding Feelings**, Chapter 5
- **Paula's Story** - from **Stories about Private Touching** in Chapter 6
- **What are Relationships?**, Chapter 7

What does your child need to learn?

Topic	Activities	Where to find them	When does the school teach this?
1. Age and stage of development	Family Photos Life Stories Growing and Changing Body Changes Stories	Chapter 1 PAGE 14 Chapter 1 PAGE 15 Chapter 6 PAGE 49 Chapter 6 PAGE 54	
2. Age appropriate behaviour	Life Stories	Chapter 1 PAGE 15	
3. Names of body parts	Laundry Basket Body Shapes	Chapter 2 PAGE 22 Chapter 2 PAGE 23	
3a. What parts are private?	Laundry Basket Body Shapes	Chapter 2 PAGE 22 Chapter 2 PAGE 23	
4. Differences between male and female	Laundry Basket Body Shapes What are Body Fluids?	Chapter 2 PAGE 22 Chapter 2 PAGE 23 Chapter 2 PAGE 26	
5. How the body works	What are Body Fluids?	Chapter 2 PAGE 26	
6. Difference between public and private places	Places	Chapter 3 PAGE 30	
7. Different behaviour is appropriate in a private place or a public place	No, That's Private	Chapter 3 PAGE 31	
8. Learning to say no to inappropriate touching of private body parts	No, That's Private What Happens Next?	Chapter 3 PAGE 31 Chapter 4 PAGE 38	

Topic	Activities	Where to find them	When does the school teach this?
9. Making choices	The Choice Chart	Chapter 4 PAGE 36	
10. Learning how to negotiate	The Choice Chart	Chapter 4 PAGE 36	
11. Strategies for saying no	What Happens Next?	Chapter 4 PAGE 38	
12. Rejecting unwanted approaches	What Happens Next?	Chapter 4 PAGE 38	
13. Recognising and naming feelings	Understanding Feelings	Chapter 5 PAGE 45	
14. Male and female body changes in adolescence	Growing and Changing Body Changes Stories - Benni Grows Up - Jenny Grows Up	Chapter 6 PAGE 49 Chapter 6 PAGE 54	
15. Learning about periods and sanitary pads	Jenny Grows Up Cara's Story	Chapter 6 PAGE 56 Chapter 6 PAGE 64	
16. Learning about wet dreams	Matt's Story	Chapter 6 PAGE 70	
17. Learning about masturbation and the importance of privacy	Paula's Story Matt's Story	Chapter 6 PAGE 68 Chapter 6 PAGE 70	
18. Learning about relationships	What are Relationships?	Chapter 7 PAGE 75	

chapter 1

The Life Cycle

THIS CHAPTER IS ABOUT understanding the stages we go through in our lives - the life cycle. It introduces the idea of growing and changing, which is the theme of this book. It will probably be where you decide to start, to provide a foundation for the rest of the book.

Growing up is all about the future: What will I be like? How will I change? What will happen to my body? This chapter will help your child to work out where he or she fits into the life cycle in relation to others and help him or her to think about the changes to expect in the future.

Decide which activity to use first. Neither of them needs privacy - having other family members join in can be very helpful. **Family Photos** on page 14 can help your child to understand where he or she fits into the family, and to show that some people are older, some younger. The **Life Stories** on page 15 explain how life moves through different stages, that people look different at different ages and can do different things. This can help your child to understand what is going to happen next.

Think about which activity may suit your child's abilities best. Will the lives described in the **Life Stories** fit what you expect for your child? If not, you can still use the stories to explain what 'growing up' involves. You can alter the stories to fit your own circumstances: your family background, religion and culture.

Family Photos works well with most young people. They enjoy the process of sorting and identifying people.

● *Helpful Hint*
Make up a story of your own which describes
what you think will be your child's experience.

Where to go next

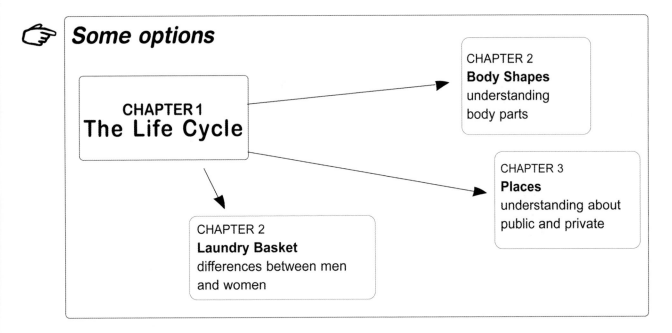

☞ **Some options**

CHAPTER 1
The Life Cycle

CHAPTER 2
Body Shapes
understanding
body parts

CHAPTER 3
Places
understanding about
public and private

CHAPTER 2
Laundry Basket
differences between men
and women

15-20 minutes with other family members too

● Family Photos

You will need

Up-to-date photographs of all your family, including as many people and generations as possible.

How to do it

- Lay all the photographs out and ask your child to name the people.
- Ask your child to arrange them with the youngest at one end of the line and the oldest at the other. Help him or her to name them in relation to himself: eg younger brother, uncle, mum, grandpa.
- Ask questions like: who are the babies, the toddlers, the children, the teenagers, the adults, the older people?
- Discuss your child's place in the line-up. What stage is he or she at now? What was he or she before? What will he or she be next?

What if...?

Your child finds this too easy?
- Try some of the ideas in **Other things you can do**, below.

Your child finds the activity too hard?
- Begin by placing the photograph of your child in the centre of the table, then picking up one other photograph at a time. Ask your child whether this person is younger or older than him or her and on which side of his or her photograph it should be placed.
- Start with just the photographs of your immediate family, and add others when your child is ready.

Other things you can do

- Group the photographs into male and female.
- Arrange them in the shape of a family tree and talk about the relationships. 'Who is Grandpa's daughter? Yes - Mum.'
- Find some photographs of family members over time to show the changes. For instance, showing dad as a baby, toddler, boy, teenager, adult. Talk about what you did at these different stages. What was your favourite toy, pop group, first girl/boyfriend? When did you leave home or buy a car?
- Use magazine pictures to see if your child can recognise the different stages for people he or she doesn't know.

10 minutes with other family members too

● Life Stories

There are two stories, one about a girl and one about a boy. The stories are told one way, but you can add your own details. You can change the names and what happens, to suit the needs, abilities and expectations of your child, your own family background, religion or culture.

You will need

The picture stories, **Mark's Story** on pages 16-17 and **Mo's Story** on pages 18-19.

 ## *How to do it*

- Decide which names you will use when telling the story. You can change 'mother' to 'mum' if you prefer it.
- Read the story through yourself, to make sure you feel comfortable with it.
- Read each part of the story while showing the relevant picture.
- You can ask your child about each sequence to see if he or she has understood eg What do babies eat? What was Mark's favourite lesson at school when he was a boy? - add details together to make the story relevant for your child.

What if...?

Your family circumstances are different from those in the story?
- Make up other simple stories to fit circumstances like those of your child, giving a range of options about the future. Mention seasons changing, holidays, when it snowed. Introduce your own family's religious festivals like Diwali or Christmas. Talk about major family events and when they happened, like moving house, a wedding, starting school, a Bar Mitzvah.
- Add your own details to **Mark's** and **Mo's Stories** eg: Do they live mainly with mum or dad or both? Do they live in care, in a large extended family or with grandma? Do they go for respite care? Do they go to church? Would Mo drive a car? What hobbies would Mark have?
- How would other children grow up - would Seema and Amarjit's lives be the same or different? Would their family backgrounds open up other choices?

You don't think your child's future will be like that in the story?
- Ask your child where he or she fits into the stages of the story. This can be a useful way to talk about your child's hopes for the future and his or her expectations about life - would it be the same as **Mark's Story** or different? eg: What did your child do when they were a baby or young child? What can he or she do now? What will your child do or be or feel when they are an adult?

Other things you can do

- Cut out pictures from magazines to make your own backgrounds for the scenes.
- Make a collage together showing the sort of future life your child expects or would like.
- Find photographs of your child from birth to the present time. Ask him or her to arrange them in order of age.

Mark's Story

1

This is Mark. He is a baby.
He sleeps a lot. His mum gives him
his milk. He likes to shake his rattle
and cuddle his teddy bear.

2

When Mark is three years old he can
run around. He makes lots of noise
playing with his toys.
He talks a bit now. He says "More"
"No!" and "I like TV". He tries to use
his potty when he has a wee.

3

Mark is eight years old and loves to
play games and talk with his friends.
He is learning lots of things at
school and likes music lessons best.

4

When Mark is 14 he speaks with a really low voice and worries when he gets spots. He likes to take a long time getting ready to go out to the youth club, checking that his hair looks good and he's wearing his cool trainers and smart shirt. He really enjoys pop music and listens to it whenever he can.

5

When Mark is 24 he has a job at a factory. He sorts out all the boxes and packages in the warehouse. Everyone likes him because he is friendly and good at his job. Mark is really strong now and can lift the heavy boxes. He goes out for long walks with his girlfriend and they meet some other friends in a café. He says no to a cigarette from one of his friends because he wants to stay healthy. He loves his girlfriend and they talk about getting married one day and having a baby.

6

When Mark is older he can't run around so quickly any more but he still keeps fit by walking, though sometimes he gets the bus home when he has big bags of shopping. He is bald because his hair has fallen out over the years. His wife loves him and their two children. Their daughter is grown up now and has a baby of her own so Mark is now a grandpa. He enjoys playing with the baby but he does like a sleep in the afternoon.

Mo's Story

1

This is Mo. She is a baby. She sleeps a lot. Her mum gives her her milk. She likes to shake her rattle and cuddle her teddy bear.

2

When Mo is three years old she can run around. She makes lots of noise playing with her toys. She talks a bit now. She says "More" "No!" and "I like TV". She tries to use her potty when she has a wee.

3

Mo is eight years old and loves to play games and talk with her friends. She is learning lots of things at school and likes music lessons best.

4

When Mo is 13 she thinks a lot about how she looks. She hates the spots on her face but she knows she will grow out of them. Her periods started a year ago, and her body is starting to look more like a grown up woman. She wears a bra now. She takes a long time getting ready to go out to the youth club, deciding which clothes to wear. She checks that her hair looks good too. She really enjoys pop music and listens to tapes on her personal stereo whenever she can.

5

When Mo is 24 she is sharing a flat with some friends. She has a job in an office. She takes phone messages and makes copies of all the papers people need. Everyone likes her because she is friendly and good at her job. Mo is much taller now. She wears make-up and earrings. She is proud of the way she looks. She goes to the pub on Saturday nights with her friends. She has a drink but says 'no' to a cigarette because she wants to stay healthy.

6

When Mo is older she has retired from work. She keeps fit by gardening, and enjoys meeting her friends at the cinema. Her hair is going grey and her face is wrinkly because she is getting older now. She likes visiting her sister Jane, especially when Jane's two grandchildren are there. They call Mo 'Great Aunty'. She loves playing with them though they do wear her out sometimes.

chapter 2
Body Parts

THIS CHAPTER IS ABOUT helping your child to learn about parts of the body - 'public' parts and 'private' parts. It includes an activity about body fluids which explains in a simple way what happens to different parts of the body, and what they are used for.

A child must be able to recognise different body parts before he or she can understand about body changes and growing up. It's important to make sure your child understands these things before you go on to the Puberty chapter (Chapter 6 – **Growing Up**). Likewise, **What are Body Fluids?** on page 26 introduces children to the idea that different fluids come out of different parts of the body. This helps them to understand later about menstruation and masturbation.

Use this chapter to help your child learn about names of body parts, including those for the opposite sex. The **What are Body Fluids?** activity is an introduction to understanding fluids like urine, semen and menstrual blood.

Decide which activity

The Laundry Basket on page 22 is a very simple activity which all young children enjoy. It can be used at home when washing or ironing clothes. It also works well with some older children who need to practise the words. The same is true of **Body Shapes** on page 23. Use **What are Body Fluids?** after **Body Shapes**, and only when your child is quite sure about body parts.

You will need to think about the words you are going to use for parts of the body. Look at the suggestions in **Which Words do we Use?** on page 76.

● *Helpful Hint*
If there are words you don't often use,
practise saying them out loud first, in private.

Where to go next

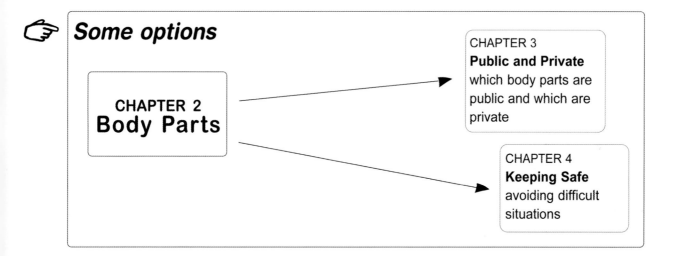

☞ *Some options*

CHAPTER 2
Body Parts

CHAPTER 3
Public and Private
which body parts are
public and which are
private

CHAPTER 4
Keeping Safe
avoiding difficult
situations

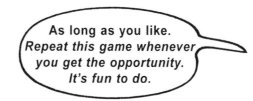
As long as you like. *Repeat this game whenever you get the opportunity.* It's fun to do.

The Laundry Basket

You will need

A collection of different clothes: for both sexes, for different ages; underwear and top clothes.

 ## How to do it

- Use this activity when you are taking the laundry out of the washing machine, or when you are hanging it up to dry, or ironing it.
- Start with an adult outer garment, like a shirt or a jumper. Hold up the garment and ask 'Who might wear this?' The answer might be a man, a woman, an adult.
- Then ask which parts of the man or woman's body it would cover. This can tell you which body part names your child knows. Continue to ask until he or she runs out of 'parts' to name.
- You can choose another garment, perhaps for a different gender, or for different parts of the body, and ask the same questions.

What if...?

Your child runs out of names, or doesn't know any?
- You can say, 'This shirt covers a man's arms/chest/shoulders' etc.

Other things you can do

- Use the same method for learning about private body parts. You can pick out underwear for this.
- Use this activity to help your child learn the difference between men and women.

15 minutes
the two of you
in private

● Body Shapes

Before you start

Decide what names you want to use for private body parts. Look at **Which Words do we Use?** on page 76 for suggestions.

You will need

The body outlines and cut-out body parts. (Pencils, tracing paper, scissors to trace and cut out the body parts).

How to do it

- Show your child the two outline drawings and ask what the drawings are meant to be. This will tell you if he or she can see that they show people.
- Ask which one is the man? Which is the woman? Introduce the words male and female.
- Start with the outline which is the same gender as your child. Ask him or her to name the parts of the body which are missing. Then using the cut-out body parts see if he or she can put the bits in the right place on the outline.
- You can show your child where they should go. You can ask what names he or she knows and tell the 'proper' names: breasts, vagina, nipples, navel, pubic hair. Don't forget the bottom and anus and clitoris even though they are not on the outline. For the male outline include penis, testicles, chest and nipples.
- Once all the body parts are in the right place, point out the differences between male and female eg both have eyes and a nose but only the male has a penis and the female a vagina.

What if...?

You or your child are embarrassed about saying the words for private body parts?
- See how quickly you can both say them without getting tongue-tied.

If your child wants to use his or her own familiar words for private body parts?
- Accept these as they are the family names but say how important it is to know the names that they will use at school or that the doctor may use.

Other things you can do

- Look at the female outline together and make a list of all the women you know.
- Using the male outline do the same for the men you know.
- Find family photographs of male and female relatives. Be clear that all women and men have these private parts but stress that this is a private matter.
- Trace over the outline onto another piece of paper and ask your child to draw on the missing parts.
- Find and cut out pictures of underwear and clothes from magazines to cover up the private parts as a way of talking about public and private. Talk about where it would be right to undress eg bathroom with the door shut, or the swimming pool changing room.

● Body Shapes

breasts and nipples

**vagina
and pubic hair**

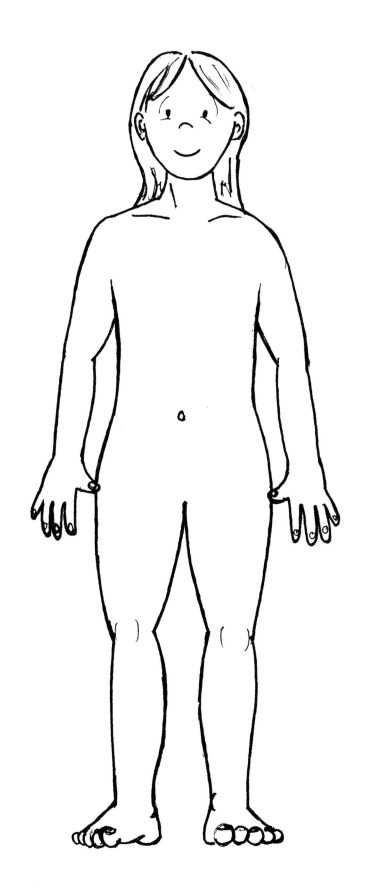

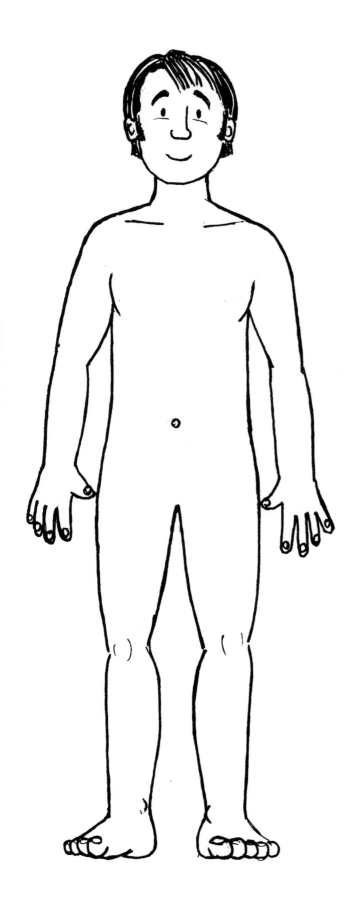

chest and nipples

**penis
and pubic hair**

testicles

15 minutes
the two of you
in private

● What are Body Fluids?

Before you start

- Find a way of feeling relaxed talking about body fluids with your child. Look at **Which Words do we Use?** (page 76) for help with using 'proper' words.
- Make sure you have done the **Body Shapes** activity on page 23 until your child is very familiar with naming body parts, and understanding public and private.

You will need

The **Body Shapes** outlines and the cut-out body parts on pages 24-25.

 ## *How to do it*

- Ask your child to place the body parts in the right places on the male and female outlines, and name them.
- Use the Body Shape which is the same gender as your child. This is how you can talk about the Body Shape of the man if your child is a boy.
  - Look at the public body parts, like the face. Use a pencil to point to the different parts of the body instead of touching the outline.
  - Ask what happens when a man cries. Explain that these are tears, and they are a fluid, or liquid, which comes out of the eyes.
  - Follow the same process for all parts of the body which produce fluid eg nose produces mucus, mouth produces saliva, armpits produce sweat, penis produces urine and semen.
  - Now discuss when these fluids are produced eg tears when sad, urine throughout the day, semen when the man's penis ejaculates.
- Do the same thing if your child is a girl, using the female body outline. In this case, tears, mucus, saliva and sweat will be the same, but urine comes from the urethra, and vaginal moisture and menstrual blood from the vagina.
- Then discuss the sort of circumstances in which these body fluids are produced eg
  - he felt upset and cried when someone was unkind to him
  - she was sweating because she was running fast to win the race

What if...?

Your child is confused?

- Go back and do the **Body Shapes** activity again, and only introduce the body fluid work gradually. For instance, make sure your child understands about tears; and then talk about tears and another fluid next time.

Your child becomes embarrassed?

- Repeat work on public and private. Explain that you will only talk about body fluids in private, and at a time agreed by both of you. Explain how important it is that your child can understand how her or his body works.

Other things you can do

- Trace the body shapes onto another piece of paper and ask your child to draw on the missing parts. Your child could also draw on the body fluids, maybe using different colours for each fluid.
- Once you are sure your child understands about the body parts of his or her own gender, then you can use the Body Shape of the other gender, in the same way.
- You can choose to link this activity with your child's own experience, and to people the child knows. You can say 'This is like mum. She has periods', or 'This is like your older brother (or sister) who goes to the toilet like you'.
- This activity can be used with other activities. **Body Changes** stories (page 54), **A Menstruation Story** (page 62) and **Stories about Private Touching** (page 66). The stories can be linked to practical hygiene in the home, like using the toilet properly or knowing what to do with sanitary pads.

chapter 3
Public and Private

THIS CHAPTER IS ABOUT understanding the difference between what is private and what is public. This applies to places and situations as well as parts of the body.

The idea of public and private is a very important one for young people with special needs to understand, and sometimes they find it difficult. Once they have grasped the idea they are more able to choose the right behaviour in different situations. This can help them not to behave in ways which can be embarrassing or worrying and may give offence.

It may help to explain a private place as 'somewhere where no-one can see you, or just walk in'. It's a complicated idea to explain. Some places can be both public and private: a door marked 'Private' in a shop may mean it's for staff only, for instance.

Decide which activity

Use these activities if your child needs to learn the difference between public and private places, in your own home and outside, and how to behave in those places. No, That's Private, the exercise on page 31 can help your child to know which parts of the body may or may not be touched in public, and gives a chance to practise a way of responding if they come across an unwelcome touch or suggestion.

Before you start, think about which parts of your home are public and which are private.

Also decide how family members' privacy is to be respected - will you decide to knock on bedroom doors, for example? And the rest of the family will need to go along with whatever is decided.

Most children can cope with these activities. If you are doing the Places activity on page 30 it may help a younger child if you use photographs of your own rooms, and places you and your child visit, to match with his or her experience.

- *Helpful Hint*
  Put large 'Private' signs on doors of private rooms.

Where to go next

Some options

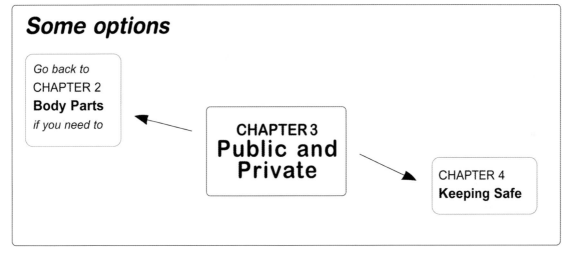

Go back to
CHAPTER 2
Body Parts
if you need to

CHAPTER 3
Public and Private

CHAPTER 4
Keeping Safe

10 minutes

● Places

Before you start

- Work out which rooms in your home are public and which are private, so that you can help your child match the pictures of places with some of the places in your own home.
- You could repeat the definition on page 28 that '**a private place is somewhere where no-one can see you, or just walk in**'.

You will need

The set of Place pictures on pages 32 and 33. The pictures can be photocopied and cut out to make the exercise easier to do.

 How to do it

- Show your child the pictures of different places and help him or her to identify them.
- Talk about what people do there - relating it to your own life. Say 'This is a supermarket. When do we go to (the name of your local shop)? What do we buy there?'
- Tell your child that some of these places are public where anyone can go.
  Ask him or her to put the pictures of these places together in a group.
- Say that some places are private, where not everyone can go. Sometimes only one person is there at a time, like a bathroom, toilet, some swimming pool changing rooms.
  Ask him or her to put these pictures into another group.
- It can be useful to keep repeating the phrases, 'This is **public**. Anyone can be here' and 'This is **private**. It's only for some people or one person.'

Other things you can do

- Wherever you go, talk about public and private places: 'Is this bus private?' 'Is our bathroom a public place?'
- Make '**Private**' signs to put up on the doors of private rooms in your home. Your child can help you to do this.

5 minutes with other family members too

No, That's Private*

Before you start

Make sure your child knows the names of body parts. Do the **Laundry Basket** and **Body Shapes** activities in Chapter 2.

You will need

The **Places** pictures, and **The Rules for Saying No** on page 34.

How to do it

- Make sure your child knows which places are public and which are private.
- Start with the picture of the street. Ask your child if he or she could touch their head in the street. Show him or her how to answer with a loud 'Yes'.
- Repeat this with other public body parts eg feet, elbows, nose.
- Now explain that you are going to ask about private body parts. Make it clear that these should not be touched in a public place like a street.
- Practise the **Rules for Saying No** on page 34
- Hold up the picture of the street. Ask your daughter 'Should you touch your vagina in the street?' Ask your son 'Should you touch your penis in the street?'
- Help your child to say 'No, that's private' following the **Rules for Saying No**.
- Repeat this with other private body parts, encouraging a loud and clear answer.
- Now use the same picture and mix up public and private body parts.

What if...?

Your child is not sure about private body parts?

- Repeat the **Body Shapes** activity, page 23. Using the body outline and the **Places** pictures, ask 'Should this woman touch her breasts in the street?' Encourage your child to answer 'No, that's private'. (But remember to emphasise that **no-one** else can touch their private parts unless they say it's OK, even if they are in a private place.)

Your child finds this activity straightforward?

- Use the other **Places** pictures and follow the same method.

Other things you can do

- Cut out pictures from magazines and match them to the **Places** pictures. For instance, match someone using a deodorant to the bathroom picture, or match someone carrying a shopping bag to the street picture.
- Use the words 'public' and 'private' as much as possible in everyday life. For example, say 'You need to be **in private**, so shut the toilet door.'
- Tell your child that if anyone tries to touch them in the wrong way, they can use **The Rules for Saying No**.
- Go on to Chapter 4 and use **What Happens Next?** to think about particular situations.

* This activity first appeared in *Let's Do It: creative activities in sex education for young people with learning disabilities.* R.Johns *et al.* Image in Action 1997

● The Places Pictures

1

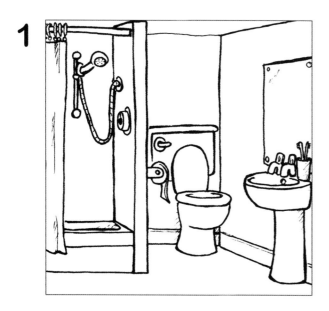

2

3

The Places Pictures

4

5

6

chapter 4
Keeping Safe

THIS CHAPTER IS ABOUT helping your child understand what to do in some of the difficult situations which can sometimes happen.

Keeping safe is one of the main things we worry about if we have a learning disabled child. We're not sure whether they will understand if someone makes unwelcome suggestions or touches. The skills needed are usually called assertion skills, to make our wishes known firmly but calmly. Here are some simple steps which we can help our child to learn.

 The Rules for Saying No
- Breathe deeply
- Stand straight and make definite eye contact
- Say no loudly and clearly
- Don't smile or laugh - be clear that saying no is serious
- Use a firm pushing away hand gesture to reinforce the words

Decide which activity

Being assertive can mean saying yes as well as no, which is why this chapter starts with **The Choice Chart**, a simple activity. It can help your child practise making positive choices about day to day matters, as well as learning about the negotiating skills needed to reach an agreement. Before you start, decide which choices you are happy for your child to make - and which not.

What Happens Next? on page 38, deals with the opposite situation - situations which could lead to difficulties. It shows how to be assertive, including some useful phrases to be used, in a range of situations shown in the picture scenes. It can also encourage discussion about the choices and decisions people have to make to keep safe, and the ways in which danger can be avoided. This is an activity best done with just the two of you the first time.

At home we can encourage our children to make choices about everyday things as they happen - watching TV for instance. Although it's easier - and usually quicker - to make the decisions ourselves, making the choice can increase children's independence. And maybe we should be pleased when our children learn to say no, if it means they can make decisions for themselves.

- *Helpful Hint*
  Bring brothers or sisters into the discussion to suggest what could be said or done.

Where to go next

 ## Some options

Chapter 5 is about feelings. You can go on to that next, or leave it until after chapter 6. Go back to any of the earlier work that needs doing again, then on to **Growing Up**!

10 minutes to start with

• The Choice Chart

Before you start

- Think about areas of choice your child can realistically have. Don't put clothing on the list unless you are prepared to agree with your child's decisions (although you may be happy to let your child choose a T-shirt every day, that may not be so for the whole outfit!).
- Explain the system to other members of your household.

You will need to copy or make a chart like the one shown on page 37, and choose your own headings. You may want to make it large enough to go on a wall, and you could use pictures as well as words for each heading.

How to do it

- Prepare the chart and put the choices you have selected in the '**Week**' spaces at the top of the chart.
- Explain the chart to your child and explain the options you have chosen. Start by choosing only one heading for the first week.
- Explain when your child will make the choices, eg every day, time of day.
- Help your child to make the first choice eg a yellow T-shirt on Monday.
- Fill in the chart together. Use words, cut-out pictures or drawings to show which choice has been made.
- Put the chart in a place where your child will see it.
- Remind your child the next day by pointing to the chart. The child chooses a second garment eg blue socks.
- Carry on for the rest of the week. Next week decide whether to choose another heading or continue with the same one.

What if...?

Your child wants to make choices about every single thing, including unwise ones like not going to school or watching TV all night?

- Go back to the chart you have made together, and point out the options you both agreed. Be firm that these are the only ones for now, although you may think about adding another one next week, for instance.
- Explain that compromise is important, and there are just some things we all have to do whether we like it or not. It is best to make healthy choices - we may want to eat nothing but chocolate, but this is unhealthy in the long term! The choices we make affect not only ourselves but often other people too.

The Choice Chart

EXAMPLE

	Week 1 Clothes	Week 2 Breakfast drink	Week 3	
Monday	Yellow T shirt	Orange juice		
Tuesday	Blue socks	Tea		

	Week 1	Week 2	Week 3	Week 4
Monday				
Tuesday				
Wednesday				
Thursday				
Friday				
Saturday				
Sunday				

10 minutes

What Happens Next?

Before you start
- Introduce **The Choice Chart** on page 37
- Practise **The Rules for Saying No** on page 34
- Do the **No, That's Private** activity on page 31.

You will need
The four picture scenes on pages 39-42.

How to do it
- Start by explaining that children need to be careful about some (nasty) adults who sometimes try to trick them by giving them sweets, or pretending they have a message from their mother.
- Take your time. You may want to start by just doing one scene and do the others another day.
- Say you are going to look at some stories about saying no and making decisions.
- Look at Scene One. Cover up Picture 2, and read the story which goes with Picture 1.
- Discuss together what Daljit could do.
- If your child has a suggestion like 'say no', ask him or her to show you how Daljit would do that. He or she can stand up and demonstrate, or you can practise doing it in turns. This helps him or her to practise the skills for themselves.
- Now uncover Picture 2 and read the text. Discuss if this is similar or different from your child's ideas.
- Ask him or her to act out what Daljit did.
- Repeat this process with the other picture scenes.

What if...?
Your child finds it too difficult?
- Go back to Chapter 3, **Public and Private**. Use the **No, That's Private** activity again until your child can say no in the right situations.

Other things you can do
- Encourage your child to make decisions. Your child will gain confidence in saying yes or no in everyday situations like which clothes to wear or which food to eat or which TV programme to watch. This can help when your child needs to be assertive in more serious or negative situations.
- Ask your child to identify adults who can be trusted in all the places he or she may go - helpful people at home, school, swimming club, shopping centre.
- You may want to encourage your child to introduce themselves to the pool lifeguard, the traffic crossing person, the local policeman or policewoman so he or she knows who to go to if close family are not around.

Keeping Safe

SCENE ONE

Daljit and the stranger

Daljit was standing at the school gate waiting for her mum to collect her. A man drove up in his car. He got out and opened the passenger door. 'I can give you a lift if you like,' he said. Daljit said 'No thank you. I don't take lifts from strangers. I'm waiting for my mum.' The man came too close to her and had his hand out as if he was going to touch her breast.

What can Daljit do?

- She can say 'No, that's private' and make a firm sign with her hand.

- Call out 'Stop. I don't know you. He's a stranger. I don't know him.' Then she can turn and walk quickly back into school and find an adult she trusts. She can tell the adult about what's happened.

Keeping Safe continued

3

SCENE TWO

John with his friends

At the weekend, John was hanging out with his friends outside their houses. An older girl from their road came up to John. She offered John what looked like a small pill or a sweet. She said 'Go on, have one. It makes you feel really good. Are you scared or what?'

4

What can John do?

This girl is not his friend. He doesn't know what the 'sweet' is.

- He can say 'No, I don't want one' or 'I'll ask my dad about this'.

- He can turn away and go back into his house to find an adult he can trust. He can tell the adult what happened.

5

SCENE THREE

Jane in the garden

Jane was sunbathing in the garden of her home. The man next door looked over the fence. He said 'I like you in your swimsuit, Jane. You really are growing up. Why don't you come over to the fence and I can rub some suntan oil in for you. Then you can have some sweets.' Jane said 'I'll ask my mum.' The man said 'Don't bother her. It can be our secret.'

6

What can Jane do?

- She can say
   'I don't keep secrets'
   'I don't want to come'
   'I always ask my mum'
   'Mum told me that secrets about touching are bad secrets'

- She can walk away quickly into her house and find an adult she trusts. She can tell the adult what happened.

7

SCENE FOUR

Mike in the shopping centre

Mike was shopping with his grandma. Mike wanders away. Then he can't see his grandma any more. He is lost.

8

What can Mike do?

- He can shout for his grandma.

- He can find a shop assistant at the till and tell her he's lost. She will help him find his grandma.

chapter 5
Feelings

THIS CHAPTER IS ABOUT recognising feelings. Sometimes our children find it hard to recognise how people are feeling - or their own feelings. The activity in this chapter helps them to identify how people feel from facial expressions.

Our feelings often change as we grow up, and teenagers can find this hard to understand and cope with. Although **Understanding Feelings** on page 45 is a very simple activity, it can lay the foundations for looking at these changes. First it helps to give names to common feelings and to talk about your child's own feelings and those of others. If you wish, and if your child is ready for it, you can carry on to talk about sexual feelings as suggested in **Other things you can do** at the bottom of page 45. Think about body language too, which also shows our feelings. Physical sensations can go along with feelings: for example we find we're breathing faster if we're scared.

For example, 'I'm feeling happy today because I've got a day off' or 'I'm feeling sad because Grandma is ill'. Even 'I'm angry because you took that biscuit from your baby brother'. And it's a good idea to show our feelings as well as talk about them. Let your child see by your actions how much you care and allow your feelings to show when you are sad or upset. This is a good opportunity to discuss with your child how groups of people from different cultures sometimes show their feelings differently, using different body language perhaps; and how people in your family group show feelings.

Understanding Feelings is a straightforward activity, but there are ideas for making it more complicated. We have used simple feelings for this activity, but there are lots more complicated feelings too. You can use this list to decide which feelings your child can recognise.

Simple	More complicated
happy	cheerful, pleased
sad	upset, depressed
frightened	anxious, scared, terrified, panicky
angry	spiteful, cross, furious
romantic	loving, emotional, passionate, sexy

● *Helpful Hint*
Tell your child how you feel in different situations.

Where to go next

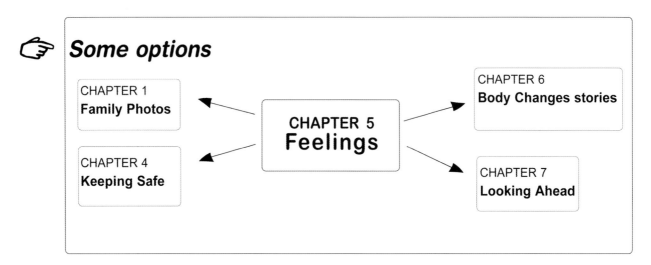

☞ **Some options**

CHAPTER 1 **Family Photos**		CHAPTER 6 **Body Changes stories**
	CHAPTER 5 **Feelings**	
CHAPTER 4 **Keeping Safe**		CHAPTER 7 **Looking Ahead**

What Happens Next?

What are Relationships?

There are links between this chapter and several others. Ask about how the characters in the different activities and stories feel about what is happening to them, or how they feel about other people.

eg   When you are telling the **Body Changes** stories in Chapter 6 you can ask how Jenny or Benni feel when they notice signs of growing up.

Use **What are Relationships?** on page 75 to develop the idea of feelings, including sexual feelings. How might each of the people in the pictures feel about one another?

10 minutes

Understanding Feelings

Before you start

Think about how you, your family and your child show their feelings. How do you use your voice, your face, and touch?

You will need the **Feelings Pictures** on page 46. They show 'happy, sad, scared, angry, romantic' feelings.

> ## *How to do it*
>
> - Show your child the 'happy' picture and ask him or her 'How does the person in this picture feel?' (If your child cannot name the feeling then you say what it is).
> - Ask how your child knows that the picture shows someone feeling happy. Talk about how the person's face looks. Talk about things like 'she is smiling'. This will encourage your child to 'read' people's faces and understand what different facial expressions mean.
> - Repeat this with the other pictures.
> - Hold up the first picture and ask 'Why might she be feeling happy? What makes people happy?' Repeat this with the other pictures.

What if...?

Your child can't recognise the feelings?
- Go through the activity from time to time, repeating the names for the feelings.
- Say things like 'I feel happy because...' when you are doing something you enjoy in all sorts of different situations.
- When your child looks happy (or angry, or whatever) say 'You look happy. Why are you happy?'

This is too easy?
- Make it more complicated by cutting out a collection of pictures from magazines, then ask your child to pick out two they think show the same feelings. You can ask them to choose two who might not like one another, or two who might like, or love, one another. Ask your child to say why he or she thinks so.

Other things you can do

- Look for pictures in magazines and compare them to the faces. See if your child can identify the feelings correctly.
- Take photos of people your child knows showing different feelings (a bit of acting is called for here!). Then he or she will have a picture of someone as a reference point when you want to discuss feelings, so you could say 'Yes, Dad is sad like in the photo - how can we cheer him up?'.
- Cut out pictures from magazines to give clues: things like - happy to be in love with a boyfriend; sad because of an accident; angry because the train is late.
- Use these feelings faces to talk about your own feelings; point to the happy face 'I feel happy when you give me a hug', 'My flowers look pretty', 'I'm watching my favourite TV programme' and then ask your child what makes him or her feel happy, sad etc.

The Feelings Pictures

PAULA HAPPY

MATT ANGRY

JOHN SAD

JENNY SCARED

CARA ROMANTIC

chapter 6
Growing Up

THIS IS WHERE you'll find all the nitty gritty bits, material about body changes, periods and masturbation. Each topic is explained in a story. Stories make it comfortable by talking about what happens to other people, so we don't have to talk about ourselves. They also make it easier to describe something which may not have happened to your child yet.

This is a time when we are forced to realise that our children are growing up, and to think about their future. We can try to show confidence so that our children can feel confident about what is happening and what will happen to them. If we help them to tackle this growing up stage positively it will prepare them for what lies ahead.

Growing up stages

Changes don't happen overnight. They can take from two to four years; any time between eight and 17 years old for girls, and about two years later for boys. Usually the first sign is getting taller, then heavier, so that body shape begins to change. Girls' breasts usually begin to grow before periods start. Body hair, and sweating, start about the same time as periods and wet dreams. Voice change and beard growth in boys are usually later. Feelings and relationships change too, and young people will need help with these as well.

Using the activities

All the stories can be used to describe and explain what happens. You could use the **Body Changes Stories** (page 54) and **A Menstruation Story** (page 62) with your child once growing or periods have begun, but it's better to tell them before this happens. This will provide reassurance, and let them know what to expect.

The **Stories About Private Touching** on page 66 are included to explain that masturbation is something to be done in private. Many young children masturbate quite naturally, but it can be embarrassing when older children do it in a public place. It doesn't help to tell a child to stop it. The best way is to help them to understand where to do it and how to keep themselves clean. But it's something you will want to think carefully about before you decide to tell the story. We don't all find it easy to talk about these things, especially within our family, although it's very helpful if we can.

Children need to know that body changes happen to everyone, to both sexes. They need to know they are normal changes; and ideally they need to know in advance.

This is another chapter where there will need to be a decision about the words to be used for private parts of the body. Look at **Which Words do we Use?** on page 76.

Your child will also need to know how hygiene matters are dealt with at home - where the clean underwear is kept, where to put dirty clothes, where to find and dispose of sanitary pads. Make sure your growing child understands where the private places are for things like changing clothes and maybe for masturbation.

Fitting the stories to your family's views

All these topics make us think about our own family culture and customs. When you are telling the stories you can change them to fit your own beliefs and views. What views does your family have about women when they have their periods, for example? And about masturbation? You can fit them to your own family circumstances. Which members of the family are available to tell these stories? Who might feel most comfortable talking about these private matters? Sometimes an aunt or uncle, or an older brother or sister, may do it best. But because of the intimate nature of these stories, we have to be aware of the vulnerability of our children, and make sure that their rights and their privacy are respected by anyone who is talking to them.

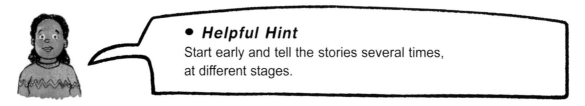

● *Helpful Hint*
Start early and tell the stories several times,
at different stages.

Where
to go
next

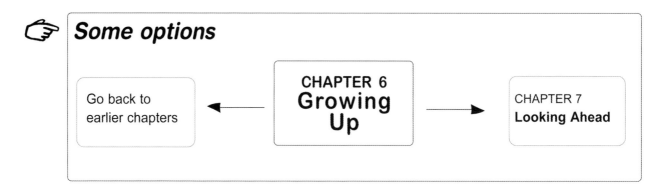

☞ *Some options*

| Go back to earlier chapters | ← | **CHAPTER 6**
Growing Up | → | CHAPTER 7
Looking Ahead |

15 minutes
the two of you
in private

Growing and Changing

Before you start

Make sure your child knows the names for public and private body parts. Use **The Laundry Basket** and the **Body Shapes** activities on pages 22 and 23.

You will need

The **Growing and Changing** picture sheets on pages 50-53.

How to do it

- Use the picture sheet which is the same gender as your child.
- Ask some general questions like 'Who is the baby?' 'Who is the oldest?' 'How is the baby different from the grown up?' 'How many parts of the body can you name?'
- Now ask questions like 'Where do I fit into the line up?' 'Where do you fit into the line up?' 'How can you tell?'
- Follow this by talking about body changes from baby to adult.

What if...?

Your child can't relate the pictures to him or herself?
- Find clothed pictures of your child at the same ages. Ask your child to match them to the right picture. Then you could match clothed pictures of other family members.

Other things you can do

- Use the other picture sheet and go through the same process. Talk about which body changes are the same and which are different for boys and girls.
- Find magazine pictures of objects for your child to match to the right age.
- Make up a story about the characters. Give them names and describe where they live, what they enjoy doing and their feelings at different stages. Link this activity with the **Life Stories** in Chapter 1.

● Growing and Changing Pictures

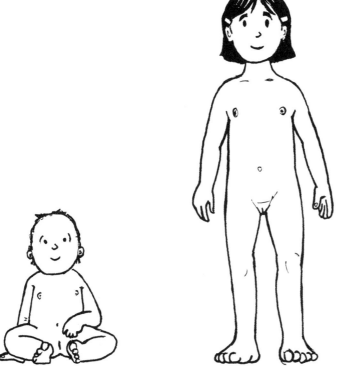

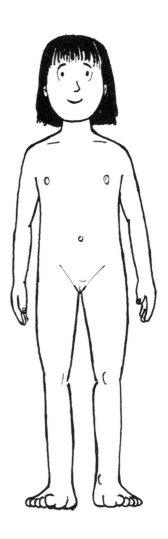

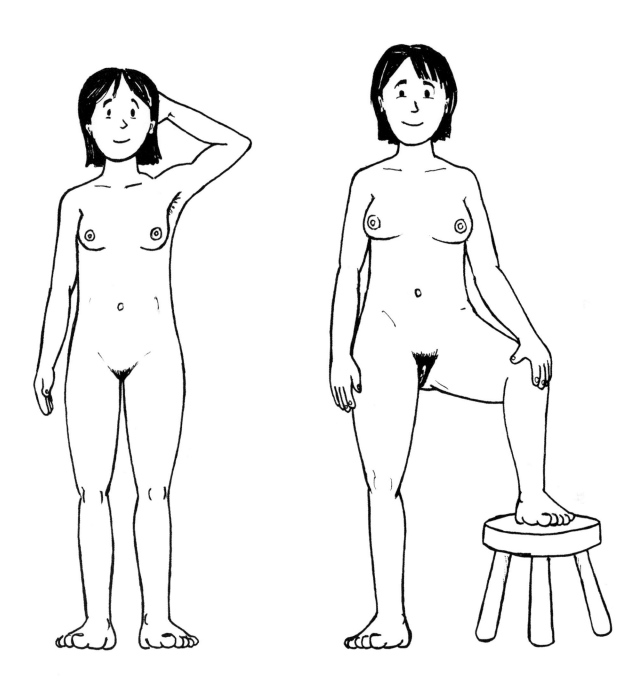

● Growing and Changing Pictures

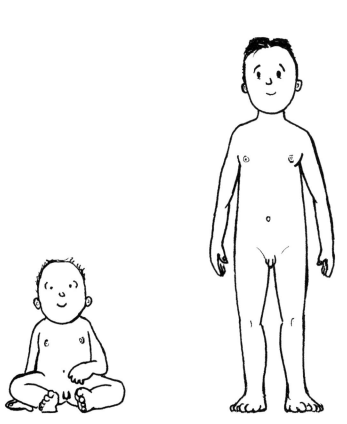
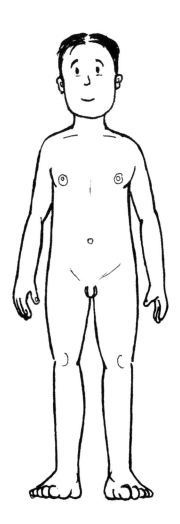

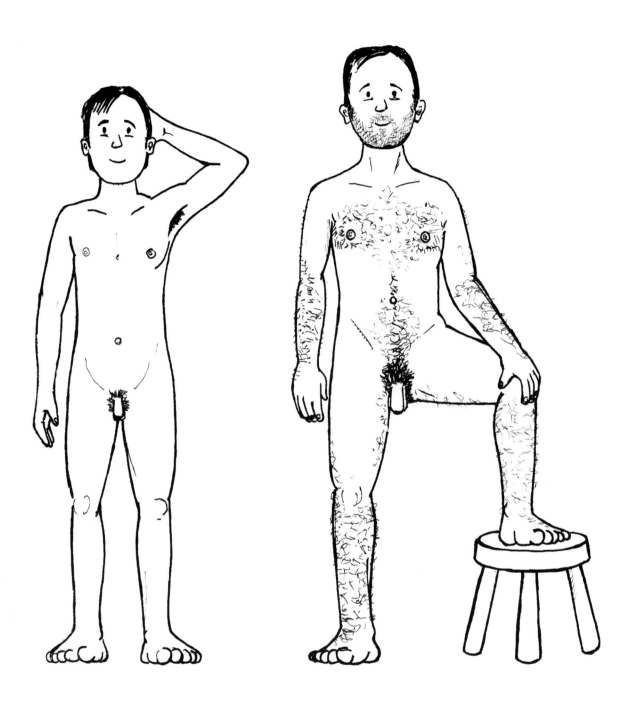

15 minutes
the two of you
in private

● The Body Changes Stories

There are two stories, Jenny's Story for girls and Benni's Story for boys.
You can tell them several times, before the changes start, and when each change
happens.

Before you start

- You may find it helpful to read some leaflets yourself about the changes that happen to girls and boys. For instance, the **fpa** leaflets *4You, 4Boys* and *4Girls*, and *Periods: what you need to know*, and others in the list on page 80.
- Make sure your child knows the information in Chapter 2 about body parts.
- Each story is divided into parts. Decide whether you want to tell each part separately or tell it all in one go.
- Think about how to introduce the story. You could say 'Soon you will be growing up into a man like your father (or a woman like your mother). This is a story about a boy (a girl) who is starting to grow up'.
- Think about who is the best person to tell the story. Who is available in your family? Is it best for dad to tell Benni's story and mum to tell Jenny's?
- Decide which names you will use when telling the story. You can change 'mother' to mum if you prefer.
- Read the story through yourself, to make sure you feel comfortable with what is in it.

You will need

The picture stories on pages 56-61.
A pack of sanitary pads for Part 2 of **Jenny's Story**.

 ## *How to do it*

- Start with the story which is for the same gender as your child.
- Tell the story one part at a time. There is probably too much to take in all at once.
- Point to the first picture and read the story for that picture. Ask questions after each picture to make sure your child has understood eg 'What is happening in the picture?' 'How does Jenny (or Benni) feel in that picture?'
- Continue to read the story, one picture at a time.

What if...?

Your child hasn't learnt about where his or her private body parts are?

- Go back to Chapter 2 to recap on body parts.
- Find out whether school has taught about this, or when they are going to.
- Look at the pictures on pages 50 and 51 in the **Growing and Changing** activity, showing a woman's vagina, and on pages 52 and 53 showing a man's penis and testicles.
- Look at the picture in the sex education book showing an erection, in picture 4 of **Matt's Story** on page 72.

Other things you can do

- When you have finished the story, show your daughter the pack of sanitary pads.
- Take her shopping to buy a pack of pads and decide together where to keep them.
- Go shopping to look at bras, even if your daughter hasn't begun to develop yet.
- Read **Cara's Story** about menstruation on page 64.
- Buy your child a deodorant and show him or her how to use it.
- Let your son watch his father or older brother shaving.
- Take him shopping to look at razors.

Jenny Grows Up

Part 1

This is a story about Jenny. Jenny is getting to the age when girls' bodies start to grow up. One day she will be a woman like her mother (or mum).

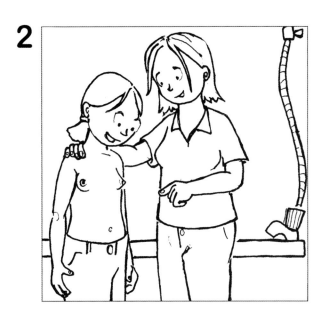

One day when she is getting dressed, she notices her chest seems to be growing, with two little bumps round her nipples. She shows her mother. She says this happens to every girl around this age, when they are growing up. The little bumps are where her breasts are beginning to grow. Soon Jenny will need to wear a bra.

Jenny's mother takes her to the shop to be measured to make sure they get the right size bra.

4

They look at several bras before they choose one which Jenny likes. She wears it proudly. Jenny knows this is a sign of growing up.

Part 2

5

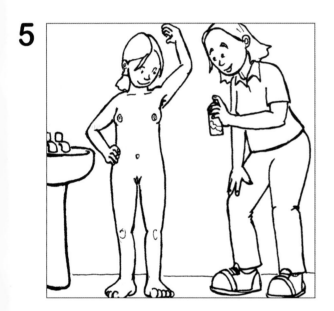

Another day, in the bath/shower, Jenny notices some little hairs between the tops of her legs. They haven't been there before and she feels a bit worried. Her mother tells her this is another sign of growing up. She also tells Jenny that hair will begin to grow under her arms. She looks under Jenny's arms and says 'Look, there are some hairs growing there already! You really are starting to grow up, Jenny. When hair grows there, girls begin to sweat. It makes your clothes damp under your arms. You can use a deodorant then.'

6

Then Jenny's mother tells Jenny that one day soon she will notice some drops of red, like blood, making a stain on her pants. A special kind of blood will come out of her vagina, between her legs, for a few days every month. Jenny will need to wear a pad then to stop the blood staining her pants. 'It's called a period,' mother says. 'It happens to most women. I wear a pad when this happens to me. I'll show you what they are like.'

7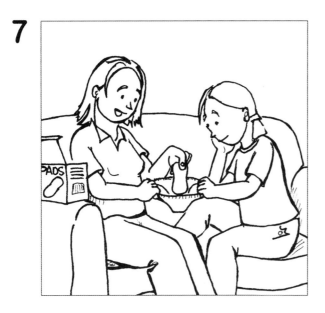

Jenny's mother gets a pack of pads and a pair of pants from the bathroom. She shows Jenny how a pad fits into the pants.

Part 3

8

'Tell me as soon as you notice any red blood in your pants,' she tells Jenny. 'Then you will need to use pads too. We'll buy a pack next time we go shopping, and you can keep them in the bathroom with mine.'

9

Jenny didn't know about periods before her mother told her. Now she feels good to know that one day she will be grown up like her mother.

Benni Grows Up

1

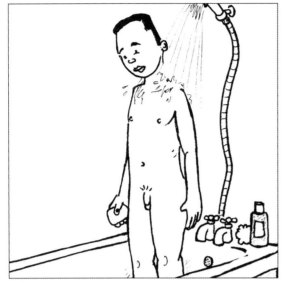

Part 1

This is a story about Benni. Benni is getting to the age when boys' bodies start to grow up. One day he will be a man like his father (or older brother).
When Benni is in the bath, he notices some little hairs between the top of his legs. They haven't been there before and he wonders what they are.

2

Benni's mother tells him this is a sign of growing up. She tells Benni that hair will begin to grow under his arms as well. Benni's father and older brother have hair under their arms and between their legs too. When she looks under Benni's arms, she says, 'Look, there are some hairs growing there already! You really are starting to grow up, Benni.'

3

His mother explains that when hairs grow there, boys begin to sweat. 'It makes your clothes damp under your arms. You can use a deodorant now.' Benni's mother shows him how to use the new deodorant. 'That will make you smell nice all day,' she says.

4

Part 2

Benni is watching his father shave one morning. 'Why do you have to do that?' he asks. His father explains that men grow hair on their faces. 'That's why some men have beards,' he says, 'but I don't want a beard so I shave it off. One day soon you will start to grow hair on your face too. We'll have to buy you your own razor ready for you to use.'

5

Benni's father takes him shopping to look at all the different types of razor. 'We'll buy you one of these simple ones to start with,' his father says. 'They're good for when you first start shaving. I'll show you how to use it when your hair begins to grow.'

Part 3

6

One day Benni is listening to some music. As he sings along with it, something funny starts to happen to Benni's voice - it goes high and then it goes low. His mother notices. She tells Benni that this is another sign that he is growing up. 'Soon your voice will settle down and be deeper like your father's (or older brother's),' she says. 'You're growing bigger now. Your voice comes from your throat, and that is growing bigger too. It makes your voice sound different.'

Part 4

7

Benni notices that his trousers are getting too short. His father talks to him about growing up. 'You're getting taller,' he says. 'That means you are growing up. Soon your body will change shape and your shoulders will get broader like mine.'

8

Benni's father thinks it is time to explain to Benni about some other parts of his body which will grow too. He tells Benni that his penis and testicles will grow as well as all the other changes which are happening to him. 'When you are a man, your penis will be bigger. It will mean that you are really grown up.'

9

Benni thinks about all the changes in his body. 'I'm going to be a man soon' he thinks, and he feels really proud.

15 minutes
the two of you
in private

A Menstruation Story

Before you start

- Check that your daughter knows about body parts and body fluids, covered in Chapter 2.
- She will also need to know about sanitary pads. You can use Part 2 of **Jenny's Story** on page 58 in **The Body Changes Stories** for this.
- Adapt this story to fit your own circumstances. For instance, about where pads are kept and disposed of, and where to find clean pants.
- Decide who is going to tell this story. If dad is bringing up his daughter alone, he may wish to find a female relative to tell the story.
- We have brought mum into the story because some young girls may not be able to cope with all these actions alone. You will know how much your daughter can manage on her own, and can adapt the story to fit.

You will need

The picture story, **Cara's Story** on pages 64-65 a pack of sanitary pads and a pair of pants.

> ## How to do it
> - Decide how to introduce the story. It will depend upon whether your daughter has already started her periods. You could say 'This is a story about periods. Grown up women have them every month. It happens to me every month, too. It will happen to you soon. It's a sign that a woman's body is grown up.' Or you could say 'This is a story about Cara. She has periods every month, like you and me.'
> - Point to the first picture and read the story for that picture.
> - Ask questions after each picture to make sure your daughter has understood.
> - Continue to read the story, one picture at a time.
> - When you have finished the story, show her the pack of sanitary pads. Take one out and show her how to put it into the pants. Then help her to do it herself.
> - Show your daughter where the pads are kept and where to put the used pads.
> - Make sure she knows where her clean pants are kept.

What if...?

Your daughter is embarrassed when you read the story?
- Say 'This is what happens to most women, every month. It's important that you get to know about what happens. Soon you will be grown up too.'
- Find out when they teach about it at school. Then you can say 'Your teacher told you about this' or 'You will soon be learning about this at school.'
- You could finish the story and then say no more at the time. Come back to it in a few weeks and see whether your daughter reacts in the same way.

Other things you can do

- Take your daughter shopping to look at packs of pads, and to buy a pack specially for her, even if she hasn't started her periods yet. They can be kept in the pre-arranged place until they are needed. Occasionally you can remind her about them, and read the story again.
- Find out what happens in school if a girl starts her first period there. Check if staff have talked to your child's class about what will happen when a girl has her period while at school. Ask about the practical arrangements.
- Some mothers take their daughters into the toilet with them when they are changing their own sanitary pad. This shows the girl what happens, and that periods are normal.

Cara's Story

1

Cara is sitting at home watching TV. Her tummy feels funny. She wants to go to the toilet.

2

Cara goes into the toilet and shuts the door. She wants to be private. She pulls her pants down. She notices there are some red marks like blood on her pants. Cara has started her period. That is why she has a pain in her tummy.

3

Cara takes her pants off. She finds the pack of sanitary pads and some clean pants in the cupboard.

4

Cara takes a sanitary pad out of the packet. She puts it into her clean pants and pulls them on. She feels clean and dry now. She washes her hands.

5

Cara tells her mother. Mum helps Cara to put the dirty pants into the sink to wash.

6

Cara goes back to the sitting room and watches her favourite programme on TV. She knows she will have a period like this every month. She is proud because she knows it means she is growing up.

> 15 minutes
> the two of you
> in private

● Stories about Private Touching

There are two stories, Matt's Story about a boy, and Paula's Story about a girl.

Before you start

- Learning about masturbation involves using words for what are very private activities. Look at **Which Words do we Use?** on page 76 for suggestions which may help.
- Your child will need to know about names of private body parts and about how they work. In Chapter 2 there is an activity, **What are Body Fluids?** which explains about vaginal moisture, semen and ejaculation.
- Part 1 of **Matt's Story** is about wet dreams. It's there to explain what happens when ejaculation takes place. This will help him to understand what happens during masturbation.
- Use the **Body Changes Stories** on pages 56-61 to explain about the body changes which take place when people grow up.
- Make sure your child understands the idea of privacy. Use the **Places** activity on page 30 to reinforce this.
- Decide where the appropriate private place is for masturbation in your home. If your child shares a bedroom, the private place might be the bathroom, or 'under the bedclothes'.

You will need

The picture stories – **Paula's Story** on pages 68-69 and **Matt's Story** on pages 70-72.

 ## How to do it

- Start with the story about your child's gender.
- Think about how to introduce the story. You might say 'This is a story about how young people learn that they must always be in private when they touch their private parts. You do this sometimes.'
- Point to the first picture and read the story for that picture.
- Ask questions after each picture to make sure your child has understood.
- Continue to read the story, one picture at a time.

What if...?

Your child is masturbating in the wrong places? (eg in the supermarket)
- Say 'In our house, the place for you to masturbate is...'
- Repeat the story emphasising the private bits.

Your child is interested but embarrassed?
- Leave the story and go back to other activities, eg about privacy and body parts.
- Leave your child to look at the story on their own.
- Use the **Life Stories** on pages 16-19 to explain that masturbation is something that younger people do when they are growing up and when they are older.

Your child isn't interested in any of this?
- Go back to other activities. Come back to this later, perhaps in a few months' time.

Other things you can do

- Make a rule for the whole family about knocking on bedroom doors, to reinforce the idea of privacy. You can put up **'Private'** signs on bedroom doors.
- Show your child the pictures of men and women's bodies changing, in **Growing and Changing** on page 49.

Paula's Story

1

Paula and her mother have been shopping. Paula has chosen a new top. She is trying it on at home and her mother says Paula looks really great and grown up.

2

Paula looks at herself in the mirror. She thinks she looks great too! She starts to touch her breasts. Her mother says 'Remember, that's a private part of your body, Paula. Only touch your breasts in private.'

3

Her mother finds a sex education book and Paula leads the way to her bedroom so they can look at it privately.

4

Paula and her mother look at the sex education book together. Paula's mother points to the picture in the book showing a woman with no clothes on. 'When a woman wants to touch her breasts and her private parts, she makes sure she is in private, alone in her bedroom,' she says.

5

GIRL TOUCHES HERSELF IN PRIVATE

The sex education book shows a picture of a young woman touching her vagina and clitoris in private. Paula's mother tells her that this can feel lovely. She says 'You are growing up, Paula. You may want to touch yourself there. That's fine, but make sure you are in a private place on your own, like your bedroom or the bathroom. Then no-one will come in.'

6

Mum leaves Paula alone in her bedroom and closes the door. Paula knows she is now in private, and she can touch her private parts if she wants to. No-one will come in.

Matt's Story

Part 1:

about wet dreams

Matt is growing up and his penis is growing larger too. Sometimes it goes hard and sticks out. One morning he wakes up and feels a small wet patch in his pyjamas. Matt is worried. He thinks he has wet the bed.

Matt calls his mother. She comes and looks at the little wet patch. She tells Matt it's nothing to worry about. 'When boys grow up, some liquid sometimes comes out of their penis. It's quite normal. It's another sign that you are growing up'. She tells Matt that this liquid is called semen, and that it sometimes comes out of the penis during the night.

Mum helps Matt to take his wet pyjamas off. She fetches a box of tissues, and explains to Matt that he will need to wipe the damp patch when he has a wet dream again. Matt knows that he hasn't wet the bed. Wet dreams are a sign of growing up. Matt is pleased now he knows he is growing up.

Part 2:

about private touching

Matt is watching television in the living room with the rest of the family. He starts rubbing his penis through his trousers. His mother notices what he is doing. She explains to him that he mustn't do this in front of other people. 'It's private touching,' she says.

Matt's mother finds a sex education book and Matt leads the way to his bedroom so they can look at it privately.

They look at the sex education book together. Matt's mother points to the picture in the book. 'When a man wants to touch his penis and his testicles, he makes sure he is in private, alone in his bedroom'.

7

The sex education book shows a picture of a young man touching his penis in private. Matt's mother explains, 'Men and boys sometimes touch their penis. Then it gets hard and semen comes out. It can give a lovely feeling.'

8

Matt's mother says, 'You are growing up, Matt. You may want to touch your penis. Make sure you are in private in your bedroom or the bathroom. If semen comes out of your penis, use tissues to clean up. Throw them away in the toilet afterwards and wash your hands.'

9

His mother leaves Matt alone in his bedroom. He feels OK touching his penis now that his mother has talked to him about it. He knows he must always do this in private.

chapter 7
Looking Ahead

Introduction

So they've reached puberty - what next? Of course, it may be sex. Sexual relationships aren't part of this book, which is about helping our children around the age of growing up. But we can't ignore our children's sexual development. It's no good putting our head in the sand and hoping sex will go away. It's when our children get to this stage that we really begin to realise that our children will grow up, and that we have to think about the future.

It's natural to worry about vulnerability and the possibility of exploitation or abuse. We may believe our children will never be able to form a sexual relationship, and we may be worried about what might happen if they do.

But whatever our abilities or disabilities, we all develop sexual feelings which may be shown in a variety of ways, in different sorts of relationships or in marriage. This means a tough task for us as parents, to help our children understand these feelings and to express them in a way which increases their well-being and does no harm to themselves or others.

Preparing for the next stage

So what can we do now to prepare our children, and ourselves, for the next stage? All parents find it hard when their teenagers approach the age of sexual maturity, but it's harder if our children have a disability.

We can help our children to increase their self-esteem and their confidence in meeting other people, by encouraging their friendships and peer group activities. We can give them plenty of practice in choosing for themselves in all sorts of situations - clothes, food, music, friends...

We can prepare them for the changes that lie ahead before they happen. Make sure they know about how their bodies and their feelings will change; about changes that happen to the opposite sex too. We can talk to them about things to do with sex when opportunities arise - maybe when watching TV, or when there is a family wedding, or a birth. We can also help them to be realistic about the choices which lie ahead, and support the choices which are possible.

We may need to prepare ourselves, before it comes to the crunch! Are we prepared to let our children take the risks which may be needed to form an intimate relationship? How do we feel about sexual relationships outside marriage, if marriage isn't an option for our child? What are our views about contraception for our sons and daughters? How easy will we find it to allow our children independence and privacy, and to leave them alone if they are developing an intimate relationship?

Your child's school will include sexual relationships in its sex education programme. Find out from the teacher what they will be doing and when. The school may have books which you can use with your child at home. Some of the books about sex for young people which are on sale in high street shops can be useful too, and you can get helpful leaflets about growing up. They are all mentioned in **For More Information** on page 80.

And let's be confident about the future. There is plenty of evidence now that many people with learning disabilities can enjoy sexual relationships which also increase their confidence and well-being. Let us help our children take this step in every way we can.

Sometimes all we need is something to start us off. To help you start thinking about these things with your child, you can use the **What are Relationships?** activity in this chapter. It provides a way in to discussion about the different people your child knows and the levels of closeness involved, with your child and between one another.

● *Helpful Hint*
Find out what the school is teaching about sex and relationships.
Ask them for ideas that you can use too.

15 minutes
the two of you
in private to
start with

What are Relationships?

Before you start

Do some of the activities in **The Life Cycle** chapter (Chapter 1) so that your child is clear about different ages, and the relationships in your own family.

You will need

A wide range of pictures of male and female people cut out from magazines, including as many differences as you can. Try to find older people and children and people from as many different ethnic groups and cultures as possible. Find pictures of people doing a range of jobs, and include pictures of people with learning disabilities if you can.

How to do it

- Choose about six different pictures and lay them out in front of your child.
- Ask your child to tell you about the person in each picture, eg old or young.
- Choose one of the pictures as the main character. Together see if you can make up relationships for that character with the people in the other five pictures.
- **For example:** A woman is the main character you have chosen. Which of the people in the other pictures is her partner, her colleague, her niece, her father, her friend, a stranger, the builder, her doctor?
- Now decide together how close is the relationship with each of these people. Discuss with your child where to place the pictures, close or far away from the main character, according to the level of the relationship. Her partner could be the closest, the stranger furthest away.
- At the end, remind your child that these are just pictures from a magazine, and the relationships are not real. Next time you do the activity they could all be different.

What if...?

Your child finds this too hard?
- Use two pictures. Agree on the main character, then ask 'Would this picture of a man be her father or her mother?'
- Use only two or three pictures to start with and make the connections yourself eg 'This is her father. This is her niece.'
- Find or take photographs of people your child knows. Do the activity with your child as the main character and place the other people near or far away from the photograph of your child.

Your child is able to do this easily?
- Make up stories for the characters and discuss how the relationships develop (see below).

Other things you can do

- Discuss the relationships of the people in the pictures by asking questions like: 'What does she like about her partner?' 'Who can she talk to most easily - the doctor or her friend?'
- Make up a story about the relationships of the main character, and talk about feelings eg 'She was angry with her partner and phoned her friend for advice' 'She was worried that her niece was ill. She took her to see the doctor who was kind and said it wasn't serious.'

chapter 8
Further Information

Which Words do we Use?

This is a real issue because there are so many different words used for body parts and sexual activity. Some of them are unique to just one family. Also these words describe very private things which we don't often talk about, especially not in public. If we are trying to help our children understand what happens when they grow up, we need to make sure we aren't confusing them by using several different words for the same thing.

Most families use their own words with their children, but schools usually decide to teach the 'proper' or biological words. Most parents want their children to know these words too, so it could be sensible to stick to the 'proper' words when we talk to our children at home. It all depends on how easy we find it ourselves to say them out loud. You will have to decide about this: and weigh up how comfortable you feel about using the 'proper' words.

We suggest you work out which words you are going to use before you start on any of the activities in the chapters about body parts, public and private, and growing up. Learning about menstruation, and particularly masturbation, involves using words for what are very private activities.

To help you, on the opposite page is a list of some of the most commonly used words for parts of the body with the biological alternatives.

Sometimes it helps to practise saying the words in front of a mirror in private so you will know when you stop going red! Another suggestion is for you and your child to see how quickly you can say a particular word without getting tongue-tied - that should stop any awkwardness!

Commonly used names	'Proper' names
boobs or tits	breasts
nips	nipples
fanny	vagina
little button	clitoris
moisture or wetness	vaginal secretion
pubes	pubic hair
belly button	navel
pee or wee	urine
wee hole	urethra
willy	penis
balls	testicles
hard on	erection
spunk	semen
come	ejaculation
wet dream	nocturnal emission
bum hole	anus
bum	bottom or buttocks

Organisations Which Can Help

- **fpa** (formerly the Family Planning Association)
  2-12 Pentonville Road
  London
  N1 9FP
  020 7837 5432 (Switchboard)
  0845 310 1334 (Helpline Monday to Friday 9am to 6pm)

- **fpa** Northern Ireland
  113 University Street
  Belfast
  BT7 1HP
  028 90325488 (Helpline Monday to Thursday 9am to 5pm, Friday 9am to 4.30pm)

- **fpa** Scotland
  Unit 10 Firhill Business Centre
  76 Firhill Road
  Glasgow
  G20 7BA
  0141 576 5088 (Helpline Monday to Thursday 9am to 5pm, Friday 9am to 4.30pm)

- **fpa** Cymru
  Suite D1
  Canton House
  435-451 Cowbridge Road East
  Cardiff CF5 1JH

  fpa produces a mail order catalogue with a comprehensive range of books and materials about contraception, sexual health and sex education, including several for people with special needs. For a free copy of the catalogue call **fpa direct** on 0845 122 8600.

fpa also runs the sexual health direct Helpline which offers confidential advice on sexual health.

- **Brook**
  421 Highgate Studios
  53-79 Highgate Road
  London NW5 1TL
  024 7654 5557 (publications)
  0800 0185 023 (information line for young people)

  Brook publishes a catalogue and books, leaflets and classroom resources on sex education, including those for young people with special needs. Its information line provides help and advice on sex and relationships.

- **Image in Action:
  sex education for young people and adults with learning disabilities**
  Chinnor Road
  Bledlow Ridge
  Buckinghamshire
  HP14 4AJ
  01494 481632

  Image in Action works with groups of young people and adults in schools, colleges and centres, publishes resources and provides training and a consultancy service for organisations providing sex education for people with learning disabilities.

- **BILD** (the British Institute of Learning Disabilities)
  Campion House
  Green Street
  Kidderminster
  Worcester
  DY10 1JL
  01562 723010

  BILD conducts research and provides information about learning disabilities. It has a mail order catalogue of books and other materials.

- **Mencap**
  123 Golden Lane
  London
  EC1Y 0RT
  0808 808 1111 (helpline)

  Provides information and advice. Contact Mencap for information about its local groups (over 400) and for details of other organisations which provide support for specific disabilities.

For More Information

There are lots of books and videos which will tell you more about sex and growing up. We have chosen a small number of them here.

Some are available from bookshops; some aren't, but we have said where you can get them. It's possible your child's school may have some of them, or your local Health Promotion Service (www.nhs.uk) has details of local services.

Some of the books listed below could be used with your children, depending on their abilities; and others you might find helpful to look at yourself. For instance, there is a lot more information about sex and puberty in the publications than we have been able to include in this book.

Books and leaflets to use with your children

From fpa

• **Periods: what you need to know**
Explains why girls have periods, what happens and how to deal with them.

• **4Boys: a below-the-belt guide to the male body**
Uses simple text and illustrations to give information on contraception and safer sex.

• **4Girls: a below-the-bra guide to the female body**
This companion booklet to *4Boys* contains facts about body changes and sexual development.

• **4You: growing up what's it all about?**
Information on puberty in a colourful cartoon booklet

• **Talking together...about sex and relationships**
Following on from *Talking together...about growing up,* this book covers greater independence, relationships, sexuality and sexual behaviour and future possibilities in adulthood. Suitable for use with young people with learning disabilities aged 13+.

From Brook

• **Girls - Looking Ahead**
Boys - Looking Ahead
Booklets covering physical and emotional changes that happen at puberty.

• **About sex: learning to love**
A set of five simple booklets: From child to adult; How a baby starts and how a baby is born; Contraception; Sex; Sex, health and infections.
Pictures with simple text for young people who have some reading ability.

From other publishers

• **Let's talk about where babies come from**
R H Harris
Walker Books
A book for young children by the same author as the highly recommended *Let's talk about sex* (see below).

• **Let's talk about sex**
R H Harris
Walker Books
Frank and reassuring about all aspects of growing up. For 10-14 year olds.

- **Now they are growing up**
  The Shepherd School, Harvey Road, Nottingham NG8 3BB, 0115 915 3265
  A set of six booklets on Menstruation, Protecting your child, Male and female masturbation, HIV and AIDS, A planned dependent life and sexuality.
  Easy-to-read booklets produced to support parents of young people with severe learning disabilities at the school.

- **Books beyond words**
  S Hollins and others
  Royal College of Psychiatrists
  020 7235 2351
  Picture books for adults with learning disabilities. For older children.

Books for parents and carers

- **Talking to your child about sex**
  fpa
  Packed with advice and support for parents and carers on how to answer questions about sex from children of all ages, from two to teens.

- **Questions children ask and how to answer them**
  M Stoppard
  Dorling Kindersley
  Covers sexuality and reproduction, relationships, religion and death.

- **Teenagers and sexuality**
  J Coleman
  Hodder and Stoughton
  A guide to understanding what happens to teenagers as they reach puberty, and their sexual development.

Books, packs and videos which your child's school may have

- **Living your life**
  A Craft, re-edited S Bustard
  Brook (024 7654 5557)
  Sex and relationships education resource. Includes modules on body changes and illustrations that can be photocopied.

- **Picture yourself**
  H Dixon and A Craft
  Me-and-Us publications (01539 621777 or www.me-and-us.com)
  Picture cards and teaching notes to help explore social and sex education with people with learning disabilities.